G000127877

1A Sequences and rules

1 Use each term-to-term rule and starting point to make a sequence with four terms in it.

   a Rule | add 3 | Start at 2.

   b Rule | add 6 | Start at 10.

   c Rule | double | Start at 3.

   d Rule | multiply by 5 | Start at 1.

   e Rule | add 100 | Start at 50.

   f Rule | multiply by 10 | Start at 6.

2 Write the next two terms in each sequence. Describe the term-to-term rule you have used.

   a 1, 3, 5, 7, …   **b** 20, 30, 40, 50, …   **c** 5, 13, 21, 29, …

   d 5, 10, 15, 20, …   **e** 6, 13, 20, 27, …   **f** 10, 110, 210, 310, …

3 Copy and complete each sequence below.

   a 2, 6, 10, …, …, 22   **b** 1, 9, …, …, 33, …

   c 9, 90, …, …, 90 000

1B Finding missing terms

1 In each of the following sequences, find the 5th and 50th terms.

   a 1, 5, 9, 13, …   **b** 3, 5, 7, 9, …   **c** 4, 12, 20, 28, …

   d 5, 15, 25, 35, …   **e** 2, 8, 14, 20, …   **f** 10, 30, 50, 70, …

   g 2, 5, 8, 11, …   **h** 0, 5, 10, 15, …   **i** 4, 11, 18, 25, …

2 In each of the following sequences, find the missing terms and the 30th term.

Term	1st	2nd	3rd	4th	5th	6th	7th	8th	…	30th
Sequence A	__	__	__	13	16	19	22	__	…	__
Sequence B	__	9	16	__	30	37	__	__	…	__
Sequence C	__	__	25	__	45	__	65	__	…	__
Sequence D	__	11	__	19	__	27	__	__	…	__

1C Function machines

1 Find the inputs and outputs for each function machine below.

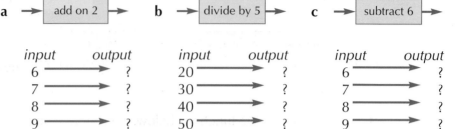

	a			b			c	
input		**output**	**input**		**output**	**input**		**output**
6	→	?	20	→	?	6	→	?
7	→	?	30	→	?	7	→	?
8	→	?	40	→	?	8	→	?
9	→	?	50	→	?	9	→	?

2 Give each function below in words.

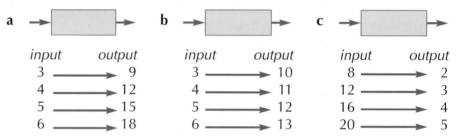

	a			b			c	
input		**output**	**input**		**output**	**input**		**output**
3	→	9	3	→	10	8	→	2
4	→	12	4	→	11	12	→	3
5	→	15	5	→	12	16	→	4
6	→	18	6	→	13	20	→	5

3 Make up your own diagrams to show each of these functions.

1D Double function machines

1 Find the outputs for each of these double function machines.

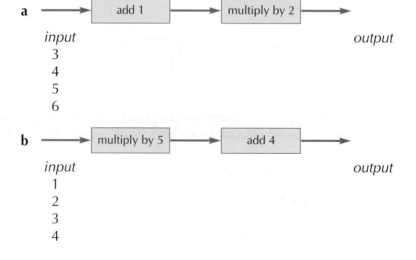

a

input	output
3	
4	
5	
6	

b

input	output
1	
2	
3	
4	

2 Draw each of these double function machines. Choose your own four input numbers for each machine.

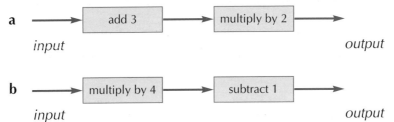

a input → add 3 → multiply by 2 → output

b input → multiply by 4 → subtract 1 → output

3 Look at the double functions below. Copy and fill in the boxes which have numbers missing.

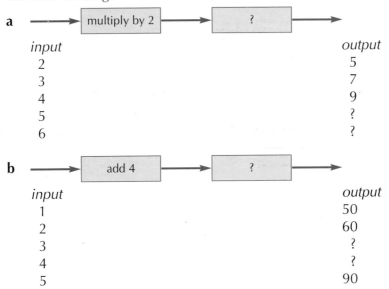

a input → multiply by 2 → ? → output

input	output
2	5
3	7
4	9
5	?
6	?

b input → add 4 → ? → output

input	output
1	50
2	60
3	?
4	?
5	90

4 Each of these functions is made up from two operations, as in Question 3. Find each double function.

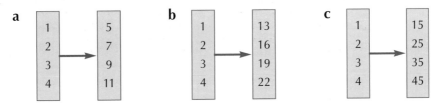

a
1	5
2	7
3	9
4	11

b
1	13
2	16
3	19
4	22

c
1	15
2	25
3	35
4	45

Practice

1E Using letter symbols to represent functions

1 Copy each function below. Then find its ouputs.

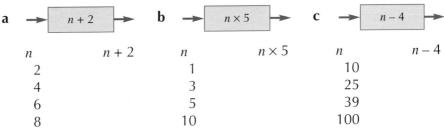

a → $n + 2$ →   **b** → $n \times 5$ →   **c** → $n - 4$ →

n	$n + 2$
2	
4	
6	
8	

n	$n \times 5$
1	
3	
5	
10	

n	$n - 4$
10	
25	
39	
100	

3

2 Write each function using *n*, as in Question 1.

a →[?]→   b →[?]→   c →[?]→

n		*n*		*n*	
1	5	10	4	3	9
2	6	11	5	5	15
3	7	12	6	7	21
4	8	13	7	9	27

3 Draw some diagrams with your own numbers to show these functions.

a →[*n* + 4]→   b →[3 × *n*]→

c →[*n* − 2]→   d →[10 × *n*]→

4 Write each function using *n*, as in Question 2.

a
8	→	12
9	→	13
10	→	14
11	→	15

b
2	→	12
3	→	18
4	→	24
5	→	30

c
8	→	2
9	→	3
10	→	4
11	→	5

d
1	→	10
2	→	20
3	→	30
4	→	40

CHAPTER 2 — Number 1

Practice

2A Decimals

1 Without using a calculator, work out:

a 1.3×10 b 0.06×10 c 68×100 d 0.7×100
e 6.4×1000 f $83 \div 10$ g $1.9 \div 10$ h $62 \div 100$
i $2.9 \div 100$ j 4.97×10 k $5.81 \div 100$ l 1.412×100

2 Fill in the missing operation.

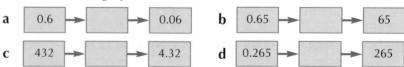

a   [0.6]→[ ]→[0.06]   b   [0.65]→[ ]→[65]

c   [432]→[ ]→[4.32]   d   [0.265]→[ ]→[265]

3 Find the missing numbers.

a $0.6 \times 100 = \boxed{}$ b $6 \div \boxed{} = 0.6$

c $0.6 \times \boxed{} = 600$ d $\boxed{} \div 100 = 0.06$

e $600 \times \boxed{} = 60\,000$ f $0.6 \div 10 = \boxed{}$

4 **a** Calculate the total cost of 100 plasters at £0.07 each.

  b Calculate the cost of this box of plugs.

  c How much does one minidisk cost?

2B Ordering whole numbers and decimals

1 **a** Copy the table on page 15 of your textbook (but not the numbers). Write these numbers in the table, getting each digit in the appropriate column.

  0.46, 0.09, 0.4, 0.38, 0.406, 0.309, 0.41

  b Use your answer to **a** to write the numbers in order from smallest to largest.

2 Write these sets of numbers in order from smallest to largest.

  a 2.382, 1.893, 2.03, 2.4, 1.86
  b 0.132, 0.031, 0.302, 0.123, 0.052

3 Put the correct sign > or < between these pairs of numbers.

  a 3.62 ... 3.26   **b** 0.07 ... 0.073   **c** £0.09 ... 10p

4 Put these amounts of money into ascending order: £1.20, 32p, £0.28, 23p, £0.63

5 Put these lengths in descending order: 57 cm, 2.05 m, 0.06 m, 123 cm, 0.9 m

6 Write the weights of these cheeses in ascending order. **Hint**: convert kilograms to grams.

785 g   0.67 kg   3.2 kg   0.652 kg   0.8 kg

2

2C Directed numbers

1 Put the correct sign > or < between these pairs of numbers.

    a −6 ... −4   **b** 5 ... −4   **c** −2 ... −8   **d** −5 ... 3

2 Work out the answer to each of these.

    a −5 + 8   **b** 2 − 7   **c** −4 − 9   **d** 2 − 6 − 3
    e −5 + 6 − 4   **f** −3 + 8 − 2   **g** 5 − 7   **h** −7 − 3
    i 4 − 6   **j** 7 − 4 + 6   **k** 2 − 5 − 8   **l** −4 − 6 +3

3 Find the missing number to make these true.

    a −5 + ☐ = −3   **b** ☐ − 3 = −7

    c ☐ − 3 = 0   **d** −2 − ☐ = 6

4 In a magic square, the numbers in any row, column or diagonal add up to give the same answer. Could this be a magic square? Give a reason for your answer.

−3		−7
	4	
	−5	

2D Estimates

1 Explain why these calculations must be wrong.

    a 53 × 21 = 1111   **b** 58 × 34 = 2972   **c** 904 ÷ 14 = 36

2 Estimate answers to each of these problems.

    a 6832 − 496   **b** 28 × 123   **c** 521 ÷ 18

    d 770 × 770   **e** $\dfrac{58.9 + 36.4}{22.5}$

3 Which is the best estimate for 15.4 × 21.6?

    a 16 × 22   **b** 15 × 21   **c** 15 × 22   **d** 16 × 21

4 **a** Football socks cost £3.71 a pair. Without working out the correct answer, could Ian buy 5 pairs using a £20 note? Explain your answer clearly.
    b Shoelaces cost 68p a pair. The shopkeeper charged Ian £3.25 for 5 pairs. Without working out the correct answer, explain why is this incorrect.

5 Estimate the number the arrow is pointing to.

    a 7 ... 9   **b** −4 ... 6   **c** 1.3 ... 2.3

2E Column method for addition and subtraction

1. By means of a drawing show how you would use a number line to work out the answers to these.

    a 4.7 + 3.8   **b** 9.3 – 3.16

2. Repeat the calculations in question 1 using column methods. Show all your working.

3. Use column methods to work out the following additions.

    a 19.8 + 23.1   **b** 28.4 + 6.92
    c 4.32 + 9.81   **d** 21.38 + 106.26 + 9.34

4. Use column methods to work out the following subtractions.

    a 17.6 – 9.4   **b** 28.6 – 12.93
    c 5.9 + 8.32 – 4.71   **d** 11.91 + 86.23 – 53.8

5. Work out the cost of a CD cleaning kit at £7.23, a CD carrying case at £5.69 and a sheet of CD labels at 84p.

6. A radio costs £26.48 and a CD player costs £52.13. How much dearer is the CD player?

2F Solving problems

1. 7 cans of beans weigh 1750 g. How much do 9 cans weigh?

2. An egg box containing 2 eggs weighs 140 g. The same egg box containing 3 eggs weighs 195 g. How much does an egg box containing 6 eggs weigh?

3. If $26 \times 152 = 3952$, write down, without calculating, the value of:

    a 2.6×152 **b** 2.6×15.2 **c** 260×1520

4. Find four consecutive even numbers that add up to 60.

5. To make a number chain, start with any number.

    If the number is even, divide it by 2 and subtract 1.
    If the number is odd, subtract 1 and double the answer.
    Investigate which numbers give the longest chains.

Practice

3A Length, perimeter and area

1 Copy each of the following and write in the missing numbers.

    a 9 cm = ... mm

    b 4.8 cm = 4 cm ... mm = ... mm

    c 5.7 cm = ... cm ... mm = ... mm

    d ... cm = ... cm ... mm = 21 mm

2 Measure the length of each of these lines.

    a _____

    b _____

    c _____

3 Measure the lengths of these pencils, giving your answers in centimetres.

    a

    b

4 Use your ruler to find the perimeters of these shapes

    a   **b**

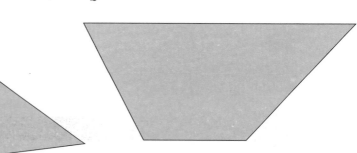

5 Copy these puzzle pieces onto 1 cm squared paper. Find the perimeter and area of each piece.

    a 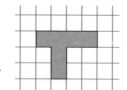   **b**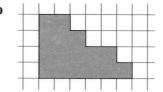

Practice

3B Perimeter and area of rectangles

1 **a** Find the perimeter of each rectangle.
   b Find the area of each rectangle.

   i
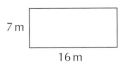
7 m

16 m

   ii

22 mm

9 mm

   iii

6 cm

6 cm

   iv 3 mm

28 mm

2 A sheet of paper measures 21 cm by 29 cm. Find the perimeter of the sheet.

3 A swimming pool is 8 m wide and 30 m long.

   a Find the perimeter of the pool.
   b Find the area of the pool.
   c Emma wants to swim 200 m.
      i How many widths does she need to swim?
      ii How many lengths does she need to swim?

4 Calculate the perimeter of this square.

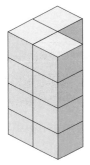
49 cm²

Practice

3C 3-D shapes

1 Find the number of cubes in each of the following 3-D shapes.

   a   **b**

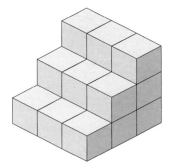

2 Three of these shapes are the same. Find the odd one out.

a

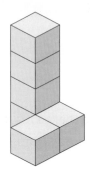

b

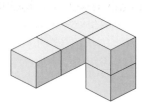

c

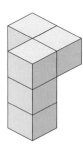

d

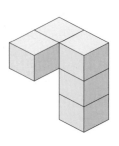

3 The net folds up to become the cuboid.

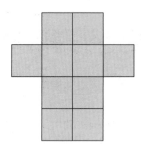
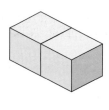

Use squared paper to draw two different nets for the cuboid.

Practice

3D Surface area of cubes

1 Find the surface area for each of the following cubes.

a

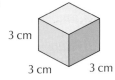

3 cm

3 cm 3 cm

b

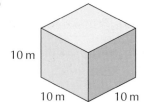

10 m

10 m 10 m

c

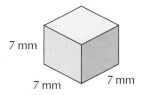

7 mm

7 mm 7 mm

2 Find the surface area for each of the cubes with the following edge lengths.

a 3 cm b 6 cm c 12 cm

3 Calculate the total surface area of the inside and outside of this jewel box, including the lid (ignore the thickness of wood).

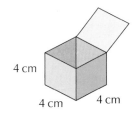

4 cm

4 cm   4 cm

4 Five unit (centimetre) cubes are placed together to make these 3-D shapes.

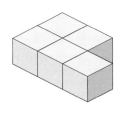

Find the surface area of each shape.

CHAPTER 4

Number 2

Practice

4A Fractions

1 Write down the fraction of each shape that is shaded.

a    **b** 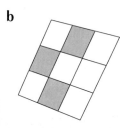   **c**    **d**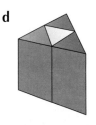

2 Draw a fraction diagram to show each fraction.

a $\frac{2}{3}$ **b** $\frac{1}{6}$ **c** $\frac{4}{5}$

3 Copy and complete the following equivalent fraction series.

$$\frac{2}{3} = \frac{4}{\square} = \frac{\square}{9} = \frac{10}{\square} = \frac{\square}{30} = \frac{60}{\square}$$

4 All of these fractions are equivalent: $\frac{1}{4} = \frac{2}{8} = \frac{5}{20}$.

Make each of the following fractions equivalent to $\frac{1}{4}$.

$$\frac{3}{\square} = \frac{10}{\square} = \frac{4}{\square} = \frac{9}{\square} = \frac{\square}{24} = \frac{\square}{28} = \frac{\square}{100} = \frac{\square}{52}$$

Practice

4B Fractions and decimals

1 Write each of these fractions as a decimal.

    a $\frac{2}{10}$ **b** eight tenths

    c $3\frac{9}{10}$ **d** two and one tenth

2 Write each of these decimals as a fraction.

    a 0.3   **b** 1.7   **c** 0.6   **d** 4.5

3 Write each of these as a decimal.

    a $\frac{23}{100}$ **b** $\frac{6}{100}$ **c** $3\frac{92}{100}$ **d** thirteen hundredths

4 Write each of these as a fraction.

    a 0.63   **b** 2.19   **c** 0.09   **d** 3.07

5 Match each decimal to an equivalent fraction.

> 0.6 $\frac{1}{4}$ $\frac{6}{100}$ 0.16 $\frac{6}{10}$ 0.25 0.06 $\frac{16}{100}$

6 Write each of these as a fraction or decimal, as appropriate.

    a 2.5   **b** $9\frac{1}{2}$ **c** 10.5   **d** $15\frac{1}{2}$

7 Write each of these as a decimal.

    a $1\frac{1}{5}$ **b** $2\frac{3}{4}$ **c** $1\frac{7}{9}$ **d** $3\frac{4}{5}$ **e** $2\frac{5}{6}$ **f** $3\frac{9}{10}$

Practice

4C Adding and subtracting fractions

1 Add the following fractions.

    a $\frac{3}{8} + \frac{1}{4}$ **b** $1\frac{1}{2} + \frac{5}{8}$ **c** $2\frac{1}{4} + 1\frac{3}{8}$ **d** $1\frac{1}{4} + \frac{7}{8} + 1\frac{1}{8}$

2 Subtract the following fractions.

    a $\frac{7}{8} - \frac{1}{4}$ **b** $1\frac{1}{2} - \frac{5}{8}$ **c** $2\frac{3}{8} - \frac{3}{4}$ **d** $3\frac{5}{8} - 1\frac{3}{4}$

3 Complete each of these statements.

    a $\frac{1}{5} + \ldots = 1$ **b** $\frac{2}{6} + \ldots = 1$ **c** $\frac{8}{9} + \ldots = 1$ **d** $\frac{6}{13} + \ldots = 1$

4 Complete each of these statements.

    a $1\frac{1}{4} + \ldots = 2$ **b** $2\frac{3}{8} + \ldots = 3$ **c** $3 - \frac{2}{7} = \ldots$

    d $4 + 2\frac{9}{10} = \ldots$ **e** $5 - 4\frac{2}{5} = \ldots$ **f** $3 - \ldots = \frac{2}{9}$

5 Convert these top heavy fractions to mixed numbers.

    a $\frac{5}{3}$ **b** $\frac{9}{2}$ **c** $\frac{10}{7}$ **d** $\frac{17}{4}$ **e** $\frac{26}{5}$ **f** $\frac{50}{9}$

6 Convert these mixed numbers to top heavy fractions.

    a $1\frac{2}{3}$ **b** $3\frac{1}{8}$ **c** $2\frac{5}{6}$ **d** $5\frac{1}{4}$ **e** $9\frac{1}{2}$ **f** $6\frac{3}{10}$

Practice

4D Equivalences

1 Work out the equivalent percentage and fraction to each of the following decimals.

    a 0.7   **b** 0.55   **c** 0.85   **d** 0.02

2 Work out the equivalent decimal and fraction to each of the following percentages.

    a 30%   **b** 15%   **c** 95%   **d** 120%

3 Work out the equivalent percentage and decimal to each of the following fractions.

    a $\frac{4}{10}$ **b** $\frac{9}{20}$ **c** $\frac{17}{20}$ **d** $\frac{3}{4}$ **e** $\frac{4}{5}$ **f** $2\frac{1}{4}$

4 Find the pairs of equivalent numbers. Write your answers like this: **m = n**.

a	b	c	d	e	f	g	h	i	j
40%	25%	0.3	0.35	90%	$\frac{2}{5}$	30%	$\frac{1}{4}$	$\frac{7}{20}$	$\frac{9}{10}$

Practice

4E Solving problems

1 Copy and complete each of these statements.

    a $\frac{4}{10}$ of 20 g = …   **b** $\frac{9}{10}$ of 60 g = …   **c** $\frac{3}{10}$ of 80 g = …
    d $\frac{1}{10}$ of 250 g= …   **e** $\frac{5}{10}$ of 300 g = …   **f** $\frac{3}{10}$ of 700 g = …

2 Copy and complete each of these statements.

    a $\frac{1}{5}$ of 40 m = …   **b** $\frac{3}{5}$ of 40 m = …   **c** $\frac{1}{3}$ of 18 m = …
    d $\frac{2}{3}$ of 21 m = …   **e** $\frac{3}{4}$ of 24 m = …   **f** $\frac{5}{8}$ of 16 m = …

3 A box contains 60 pencils. $\frac{3}{4}$ are given out to pupils. How many are given out?

4 Copy and complete each of these statements.

    a 50% of 30 kg = ...   **b** 25% of 12 kg = ...
    c 50% of 120 kg = ...   **d** 25% of 96 kg = ...

5 Work out the following.

    a One-quarter of thirty-two.   **b** One-seventh of forty-nine.
    c One-tenth of two hundred and fifty.

6 Work out the following.

    a $\frac{1}{4}$ of £60   **b** $\frac{3}{5}$ of 30 kg   **c** $\frac{4}{7}$ of 56 m   **d** $\frac{8}{9}$ of 63p

CHAPTER 5   Handling Data 1

Practice

5A Mode and range

1 Find the mode of the following sets of data.

    a win, draw, win, lose, lose, draw, win, draw, lose, lose, draw, win, draw
    b ⇔ ⇓ ⇑ ⇒ ⇓ ⇐ ⇓ ⇒ ⇑ ⇔

2 For the following sets of data, find the mode, if possible.

    a 2, 7, 3, 12, 9, 15, 3
    b 5, 1, 7, 7, 3, 1, 5, 2, 6, 5, 3, 2, 4, 9
    c 31, 19, 17, 28, 40, 30, 42, 7

3 Find the range for each of the following sets of data.

    a 20, 70, 30, 25, 90, 35, 60, 60, 15
    b 3.1, 5.6, 2.9, 4.8, 3.6, 4.9, 6.3, 3.7

4 Find the mode, median and range for each of the following sets of data.

    a 200 mm, 150 mm, 600 mm, 300 mm, 450 mm, 200 mm, 500 mm, 250 mm, 550 mm
    b £3.20   £2.90   £3.10   £3   £3.15   £2.90
    c 58 g, 48 g, 48 g, 52 g, 50 g, 51 g, 50 g, 56 g, 48 g, 58 g, 52 g, 56 g

5 17 cars of the same year and model were tested for fuel efficiency. The table shows the miles per gallon (mpg) for the cars.

mpg	36	37	38	39	40
Number of cars (frequency)	3	4	7	2	1

    a Calculate the mode.
    b Calculate the median.
    c Calculate the range.

6 The table shows the sizes of 'breaks' during a snooker club tournament.

Break	Tally	Frequency
1 – 10	𝍷𝍷𝍷 𝍷𝍷𝍷 ///	
11 – 20	𝍷𝍷𝍷 𝍷𝍷𝍷 𝍷𝍷𝍷 𝍷𝍷𝍷 𝍷𝍷𝍷	
21 – 30	𝍷𝍷𝍷 /	
31 – 40	////	
41 – 50	//	

a Fill in the frequency column.
b Which is the modal class?
c What is the maximum possible range?

7 a Write down five numbers with a mode of 3 and range 4.
b Write down five numbers with a mode of 10 and range 5.

Practice

5B Reading data from tables and charts

1 The table shows the tallest waterfalls in the world.

Name	Height (m)	Location
Pilao	524	Brazil
Cleve-Garth	450	New Zealand
Ribbon	491	USA
Itatinga	628	Brazil
Roraima	457	Guyana
Angel (upper fall)	807	Venezuela
Ormeli	563	Norway
Cuquenan	610	Guyana-Venezuela
Tysse	533	Norway
Vestre Mardola	468	Norway

a How tall is the Ribbon waterfall?
b Which waterfalls are shorter than the Ribbon waterfall?
c Which is the shortest waterfall? Where is it?
d Which is the shortest waterfall in Brazil?
e How much taller is the Cuquenan waterfall than the Ribbon waterfall?

5

2 The table shows the road distances between some European cities and towns.

Athens

3300	Barcelona				
3000	1300	Brussels			
3200	1300	200	Calais		
3300	1300	600	500	Cherbourg	
2800	1500	200	400	800	Cologne

a What is the distance between these places.
   i Athens and Brussels   ii Cherbourg and Barcelona
b Which places are closest together?
c Farouk travels from Calais to Cherbourg to Athens and back to Calais. How far does he travel altogether?

3 A postmaster recorded the 1p to 5p stamps sold at his post office one morning.

5 1 1 2 4 1 5 1 3 5 2 4 1 2 1 5 1 5 1 5
1 4 5 1 1 2 5 1 5 2

4 a Copy and complete the tally chart

Value of Stamp (p)	Tally	Frequency
1		
2		
3		
4		
5		

b Write down the mode for the data.
c Write down the range for the data.
d Draw a line bar graph for the data.

Practice
5C Statistical diagrams

1 The pictogram shows how far some cyclists travelled in the London to Brighton bike ride.

Julian

Marcus

Terri

Rabi

Key: ⬤ = 10 miles

a How far did Julian cycle?
b Marcus completed the ride. How far is London from Brighton?
c Who cycled half the distance?
d How far did Terri Cycle?
e How far did the cyclists travel altogether?

2 The dual bar chart shows car sales for two showrooms, Connors and VPW.

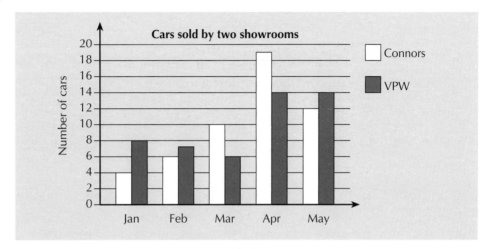

a Which showroom sold the most cars?
b During how many months did Connors sell more cars than VPW?
c Give the record number of cars sold by each showroom in any month.
d What is the range of cars sold for each showroom?

3 The grouped bar chart below shows the lifetimes of some batteries in a test.

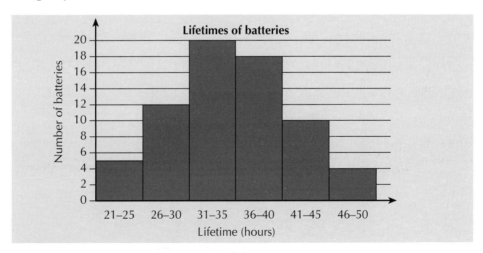

a Make a frequency table for the data.
b What is the modal class?
c What was the total number of batteries tested?
d How many batteries had a lifetime of 40 hours or less?

4 Jan checks the fuel in her motorbike tank at the end of each day. The line graph below shows the fuel levels for one week.

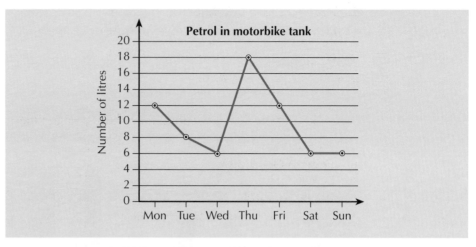

a How much fuel was in the tank at the end of Friday?
b When did the tank contain 6 litres of fuel?
c On which day was the tank refilled?
d What is the range of fuel in the tank for the week?
e On which day did Jan not use her motorbike?

Practice

5D Probability

1 Choose one of the following words which best describes the probability for the events below.

impossible, very unlikely, unlikely, evens, likely, very likely, certain

a A bonfire will cause smoke.
b A telephone number ends with an odd digit.
c A cup will break if it is dropped.
d A 7 is thrown using an ordinary dice.
e A letter will get lost in the post.

2 Sweets contained in a bag of 'Lucky Numbers' are shown below.

a One sweet is picked from the bag, at random. What is the probability the number is:
   i odd   **ii** greater than 5   **iii** odd or even   **iv** a multiple of 3?
b Which number has a probability of $\frac{1}{5}$ of being picked?

3 Mark has these chopsticks in his kitchen drawer.

Short	Long
6 red	2 red
2 green	8 green
4 yellow	2 yellow

He picks a chopstick at random. Find these probabilities.

a P(red)
b P(green or yellow)
c P(short)
d P(long and red)
e P(short and red **or** short and yellow)

4 Sema has made a Wheel of Fortune game.
It costs 5p to play. The numbers on the wheel
show the prizes, in pence.

If the wheel is spun once, what is the
probability of winning the following prizes?
Express your answers as decimals.

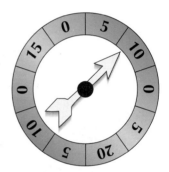

a 10p **b** nothing
c more than 5p **d** the biggest prize
e 7p

Practice

5E Experimental probability

1 a Toss a die 50 times and record your results in a frequency table.
b Find the experimental probability of getting a 6, writing your answer as:
   i a fraction
   ii a decimal.
c If you repeated the experiment, would you get the same results?

2 a Trace this spinner and cut it
out of thin card or paper. Push
a drawing pin through the
centre.
b Spin your spinner 50 times.
Record your results in a
frequency table.
c Calculate the experimental
probability of the spinner
landing on a letter.
d Is your answer greater or less
than even chance?

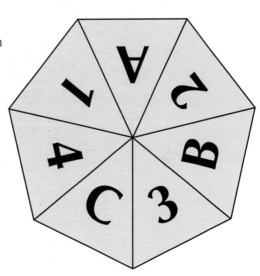

3 These three coins were flipped together. Two of the coins are Tails.

a Copy the tally chart below.

Result	Tally	Frequency
Two tails		
Other		

b Flip three coins 30 times. Record the results in the tally chart.
c Calculate the experimental probability of getting two tails.
d Is your answer greater or less than even chance?

CHAPTER 6 Algebra 2

Practice

6A Finding unknown numbers

1 Copy and complete the following, replacing □ with a number to make each addition correct.

a $3 + \square = 7$ **b** $\square + 10 = 11$ **c** $\square + 9 = 27$
d $12 + \square = 17$

2 Copy and complete the following, replacing ▲ with a number to make each multiplication correct.

a $9 \times \blacktriangle = 27$ **b** $\blacktriangle \times 7 = 35$ **c** $10 \times \blacktriangle = 70$
d $\blacktriangle \times 8 = 64$

3 Copy and complete the following, replacing ■ with a number to make each subtraction correct.

a $12 - \blacksquare = 9$ **b** $\blacksquare - 6 = 4$ **c** $20 - \blacksquare = 2$
d $\blacksquare - 7 = 15$

4 Find the number the shape represents.

a $4 + \blacksquare = 12$ **b** $3 \times \blacktriangle = 21$ **c** $\blacklozenge - 8 = 8$
d $\blacktriangle \times 6 = 36$ **e** $\blacksquare + 12 = 19$ **f** $17 - \blacklozenge = 7$

5 Copy each Crossnumber puzzle. Fill in the empty squares to make the equations true. Start with the bold square.

2	+		=	12
×	■	–	■	+
=	■	=	■	=
32	–	7	=	

		–		=	
+	■	+		×
3	–		=	2
=	■	=		=
		–	12	=	4

6		5	=	
–	■	×	■	–
	+		=	9
=	■	=		=
	+	20	=	

Practice

6B Calculating using rules

1 A film is recorded onto a video tape. The recording time left can be calculated by the rule:

Time left on tape = Length of tape – Length of film

Calculate the time left on these tapes.

a 240 minute tape after recording Jeepers lasting 80 minutes.
b 180 minute tape after recording Deep Water lasting 115 minutes.

2 Use this rule to convert British Pounds (£) to US dollars ($):

Number of British Pounds = $1\frac{1}{2}$ times Number of US dollars

Convert these amounts.

a £20 **b** £100 **c** £6

3 The total cost of an artist's paint box is calculated by the rule:

Total cost = £2 for the box plus 50p for each tube of paint

Calculate the total cost of the following.

a Box containing 8 tubes of paint.
b Box containing 15 tubes of paint.

4 The length of a wall is given by the formula:

Length of wall = Area of wall divided by Height of wall

Use the formula to find the lengths of these walls.

a Area = 12 m², height = 2 m **b** Area = 40 m², height = 8 m

6C Algebraic terms and expressions

1 Write terms, or expressions to illustrate the following sentences.

a Add 4 to x.   **b** Divide y by 2.

c Multiply p by 7.   **d** E minus t.

e Multiply 2 by c.   **f** Subtract a from 5.

2 Write down the value of each expression for the three values of m.

a $m - 3$ where   **i** $m = 3$ **ii** $m = 10$ **iii** $m = 17$

b $m + 10$ where   **i** $m = 4$ **ii** $m = 9$ **iii** $m = 20$

c $m + 6$ where   **i** $m = 4$ **ii** $m = 18$ **iii** $m = 40$

d $m - 5$ where   **i** $m = 10$ **ii** $m = 25$ **iii** $m = 100$

3 Write down the value of each expression for the three values of c.

a $4c$ where   **i** $c = 2$ **ii** $c = 5$ **iii** $c = 10$

b $7c$ where   **i** $c = 6$ **ii** $c = 10$ **iii** $c = 12$

c $20c$ where   **i** $c = 1$ **ii** $c = 3$ **iii** $c = 10$

4 Write down the value of each expression for the three values of p.

a $2 + p$ where   **i** $p = 5$ **ii** $p = 8$ **iii** $p = 13$

b $9 - p$ where   **i** $p = 2$ **ii** $p = 6$ **iii** $p = 9$

c $20 - p$ where   **i** $p = 1$ **ii** $p = 7$ **iii** $p = 18$

5 Which expression has the greatest value?

a
$2x$ where $x = 9$

b
$t - 3$ where $t = 20$

c
$18 - r$ where $r = 6$

d
$d + 11$ where $d = 4$

6D Formulae

1 Write each of these rules as a formula. The variables are printed in bold.

a The total **c**ost of a number of 10p **s**tamps.

b The **c**eiling height is the **d**oor height plus 1 m.

c The **t**otal weight of 5 **b**ricks.

2 A builder uses this formula to mix mortar:

$$S = 6c$$

where S = number of shovels of sand
    c = number of shovels of cement

Use the formula to calculate the sand mixed with:

a 3 shovels of cement   **b** 5 shovels of cement
c 8 shovels of cement

3 Mark uses this formula to share some winnings between friends:

$$A = 60 \div F$$

where F = number of friends
    A = amount each friend receives, in £

Calculate the amount each friend receives when there are:

a 3 friends   **b** 4 friends   **c** 6 friends

4 The total cost of getting a car through the MOT is given by the formula:

$$C = R + 25$$

where R = cost of repairs, in £
    C = total cost, in £

Find the total cost when:

a R = £50   **b** R = £110   **c** R = £0

Practice

6E Equations

1 Solve the following equations.

a $5x = 20$ **b** $10y = 10$ **c** $8p = 32$ **d** $9d = 72$
e $2q = 300$ **f** $7n = 154$ **g** $3r = 81$ **h** $4t = 240$

2 Solve the following equations.

a $p + 5 = 12$ **b** $m + 8 = 17$ **c** $b + 30 = 100$
d $h + 16 = 32$ **e** $d - 3 = 8$ **f** $p - 9 = 12$
g $m - 23 = 17$ **h** $s - 40 = 170$

3 Solve the following equations.

a $2y + 1 = 11$ **b** $3b + 2 = 14$ **c** $7x + 6 = 41$
d $10p + 40 = 100$ **e** $6q + 8 = 56$ **f** $2m + 100 = 400$
g $5d + 17 = 52$ **h** $8r + 28 = 92$

4 Solve the following equations.

a $4m - 3 = 13$ b $2q - 7 = 11$ c $5v - 10 = 25$
d $7n - 13 = 8$ e $10A - 60 = 100$ f $2w - 35 = 35$
g $6f - 18 = 36$ h $11x - 17 = 49$

5 Two of these equations have the same solution. Find them. Write down the solutions to all of the equations.

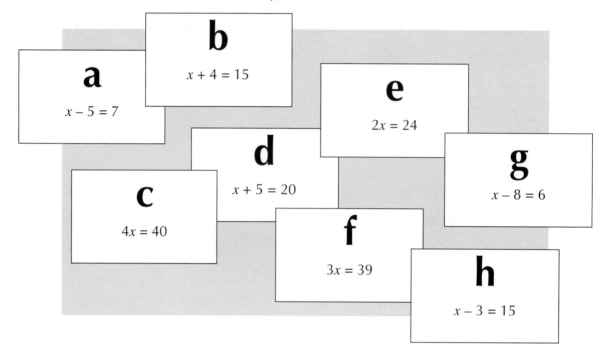

b $x + 4 = 15$

a $x - 5 = 7$

e $2x = 24$

d $x + 5 = 20$

g $x - 8 = 6$

c $4x = 40$

f $3x = 39$

h $x - 3 = 15$

CHAPTER 7 Shape, Space and Measures 2

Practice

7A Lines and angles

1 Describe the following turns.

a 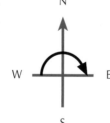 b 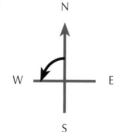 c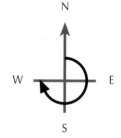

2 Copy and complete the following table.

	Starting direction	Amount of turn	Finishing direction
a	West	$\frac{1}{2}$ turn clockwise	
b	North	$\frac{1}{4}$ turn anticlockwise	
c	East	$\frac{3}{4}$ turn clockwise	

3 Describe each angle as acute, right-angle or obtuse. Estimate the size of each angle.

a **b** **c** **d**

4 For the shape ABCDEF:

   a Write down two lines that are equal in length.
   b Write down two lines that are parallel.
   c Write down two lines that are perpendicular.

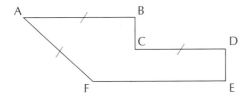

5 Write down the geometric properties of this kite.

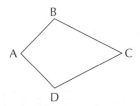

7B Calculating angles

Calculate the size of each unknown angle.

1 a   **b**

2 a   **b**   **c**

3 **a**   **b** 15°   **c**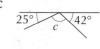

4 **a**   **b**   **c**

7C Coordinates

1 Write down the coordinates of points
A, B, C, D and E on the grid.

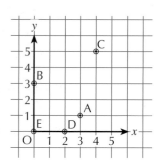

2 **a** Make a copy of the grid in question 1 and plot
the points A(1, 1), B(3, 1) and C(5, 4).
   b The three points are the corners of a
parallelogram. Plot the point D to complete the
parallelogram.

3 The diagram shows the plan of a garden.

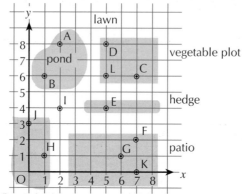

a Write down the coordinates of the marked points in the:
   i pond   **ii** vegetable plot   **iii** hedge   **iv** flower bed
   v patio   **vi** lawn.
b Where is each of these points?
   i (4, 4)   **ii** (3, 8)   **iii** (8, 3)   **iv** (6, 8)   **v** the origin
   vi (0, 7)   **vii** (3, 0)

CHAPTER 8 Handling Data 2

Practice

8A Using a tally chart

Local residents were asked how they would like to see some waste ground developed. The results are shown in the tally chart below.

Development	Tally	Frequency
Swimming pool	𝍸𝍸 /	
Playground	𝍸𝍸 𝍸𝍸 //	
Supermarket	𝍸𝍸 ////	
Health centre	𝍸𝍸	
Cafe	///	

1 Draw a bar chart to illustrate the data.

2 Write possible reasons why the residents voted for each kind of development.

Practice

8B Using the correct data

You are going to investigate the number of words per line in a paperback novel. Follow these steps:

1 Copy this tally chart. You will need 10 to 15 rows.

Number of words	Tally	Frequency
1		
2		
3		
4		

2 Find a paperback novel. Choose a page at random. Count the number of words on each line. Do this for 50 lines. Record the data in your tally chart.

3 Decide how to count hyphenated words, numbers, etc.

4 Draw a bar chart to illustrate your data.

5 If you have time, repeat the activity using a different paperback. Compare your results.

1 Some pupils were asked how many music CDs they owned. The results are shown below.

14	1	4	7	0	11	7	2	17	9
20	6	10	0	5	3	21	0	15	6
11	0	13	3	8	2	18	9	27	1
12	8	1	18						

a Copy and complete this grouped frequency table.

Number of CDs	Tally	Frequency
0–4		
5–9		
10–14		
15–19		
20–24		
...		

b Draw a bar chart to illustrate the data.

2 The average ages of families at a small holiday resort are shown below.

31	17	31	21	32	29	27	39	25	25
40	27	36	28	46	19	38	32	23	28
35	19	41	30	24	34	55	26	20	36
43	51								

a Which is the most sensible table for the data? Explain your answer.

Average age	Tally	Frequency
10–14		
15–20		
...		

Average age	Tally	Frequency
0–19		
20–39		
...		

Average age	Tally	Frequency
10–19		
20–29		
...		

b Copy and complete the table you chose in part **a**.
c Draw a bar chart to illustrate the data.

Kickoff Ltd closes down during the summer holiday. Office and factory staff were asked these questions about their preferred holiday times.

'How many days of your annual leave would you like to use for your summer holiday?'
'In which month would you like your summer holiday?'
'On which day of the week should the holiday begin?'

Their answers are shown in the table below.

Employee	Male/Female	Days of annual leave	Month	Weekday
Office	M	10	June	Monday
Office	F	5	August	Monday
Factory	M	5	August	Wednesday
Office	M	10	June	Monday
Factory	F	8	July	Wednesday
Factory	M	12	August	Thursday
Factory	M	10	July	Monday
Office	F	10	August	Monday
Factory	F	5	July	Wednesday
Factory	F	15	July	Monday
Factory	M	10	June	Monday
Factory	F	5	August	Monday
Factory	M	10	August	Monday
Office	F	12	July	Thursday
Factory	F	10	August	Monday
Factory	M	5	August	Monday
Factory	F	5	July	Friday
Office	F	10	June	Monday
Office	M	5	August	Wednesday
Factory	F	10	July	Monday

1 a Make a frequency table for the number of days chosen by office staff.
  b Make a frequency table for the number of days chosen by factory staff.
  c Write a sentence comparing office and factory staff.

2 a Make a frequency table for the holiday months chosen by male staff.
  b Make a frequency table for the holiday months chosen by female staff.
  c Write a sentence comparing male and female staff.

3 a Make a frequency table for the start day chosen by office staff.
  b Make a frequency table for the start day chosen by factory staff.
  c Write a sentence comparing office and factory staff.

4 Think of another question about staff holidays. Write it down as you would on a data collection sheet, i.e. using answer boxes.

CHAPTER 9

Number and Measures 3

9A Rounding

1 Round off these numbers to:
 i the nearest 10 **ii** the nearest 100 **iii** the nearest 1000.

 a 657 **b** 2555 **c** 3945 **d** 409 **e** 17 059 **f** 9895

2 Round off these numbers to:
 i the nearest whole number **ii** one decimal place.

 a 7.32 **b** 8.75 **c** 3.04 **d** 19.58 **e** 0.749 **f** 9.955

3 **i** What are these Test Your Strength scores, to the nearest 100?
 ii Estimate the scores to the nearest 10.

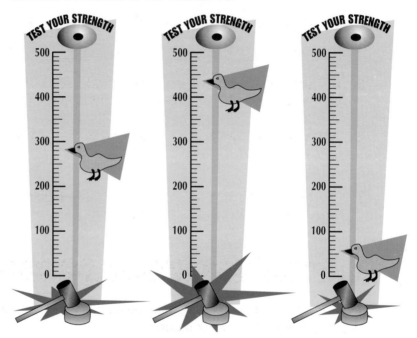

4 **i** Read these weighing scales, to the nearest gram.
 ii Read the scales to the nearest 10 g.
 iii Read the scales, correct to one decimal place

5 Round these bank balances using a sensible degree of accuracy. Then place them in order of size, starting with the smallest.

Andrew	**£4960.78**	Jamil	**£680**	Geoff	**£4799.50**
Jean	**£12 600**	Suzy	**£6709.67**	Laurence	**£94.45**
Harry	**£6921.44**	Sema	**£4934.24**	Darren	**£5094.68**

Practice

9B The four operations

1 Write down the answer to each of these.

  a 5×4 **b** 8×7 **c** 3×9 **d** 8×4
  e 7×6 **f** 2×9 **g** 8×5 **h** 0×7

2 Work out these.

  a 7×30 **b** 9×80 **c** 50×6 **d** 3×700
  e 60×4 **f** 30×20

3 Copy each of these grids and fill in the gaps.

  a 51×6

×	50	1
6		

  b 37×8

×	30	7
8		

4 Work out these. Use the grid method in Question 3, or any other method.

  a 42×6 **b** 28×9 **c** 33×8 **d** 59×5

5 **a** Two consecutive integers have a product of 210. What are they?
  b Three consecutive numbers have a sum of 66. What are they?

6 A train leaves Pushton at 13.35 and arrives at Dudley at 14.15. How long was the journey?

7 A train leaves Pinkton at 7:50. It arrives at Georgetown 32 minutes later. At what time does it arrive in Georgetown?

Practice

9C BODMAS

1 Copy these calculations. Circle the operation that you do first in these calculations, then work it out.

  a $9 - 6 \div 3$ **b** $3 \times (20 - 15)$ **c** $50 \div 10 - 5$
  d $(3 + 13) \div 4$

2 Work out the following showing each step of the calculation.

  a $20 + 20 \div 4$ **b** $4 \times 8 - 3 \times 7$ **c** $(8 - 2) \times 4$
  d $(8 + 12) \div 4$

3 Copy these calculations. Put brackets into the calculations to make them true.

  a $20 - 10 - 3 = 13$ **b** $5 + 2 \times 2 = 14$
  c $9 - 7 - 5 - 3 = 4$ **d** $5 - 2^2 = 9$
  e $12 - 3 \times 10 - 6 = 0$ **f** $10 + 10 \div 10 + 10 = 1$
  g $1 + 3^2 + 5^2 = 41$ **h** $40 - 20 \div 4 + 1 = 36$

4 Work out the value of each expression in your head.

   a $5 + (2 \times 7)$ **b** $(6 + 8) \div 2$ **c** $(9 \times 6) - 10$
   d $20 - (10 - 8)$ **e** $4 \times (5 + 7)$ **f** $24 \div (3 + 5)$

Practice

9D Multiplication and division

1 Work out the following multiplication problems. Use any method you are happy with.

   a 13×3 **b** 54×7 **c** 148×3 **d** 9×275

2 Work out each division by subtracting multiples.

   a $56 \div 5$ **b** $93 \div 7$ **c** $132 \div 8$

3 Work out the following division problems. Use any method you are happy with. Some of the problems will have a remainder.

   a $152 \div 4$ **b** $345 \div 6$ **c** $195 \div 5$ **d** $306 \div 8$

Decide whether the following problems involve multiplication or division. Then do the appropriate calculation, showing your method clearly.

4 A cinema has 23 rows of seats. Each row has 8 seats. How many people can be seated in the cinema?

5 A bag contains 234 g of sugar. The sugar is used to make sweets. Each sweet contains 9 g of sugar.

   a How many sweets were made?
   b How much sugar is needed to make 173 sweets?

6 Metal screws weigh 7 g each.

   a How many can be made from a block of metal weighing 326 g?
   b How much does a pack of 134 screws weigh?

Practice

9E Efficient calculations

1 Work out each of these.

   a 9×10 **b** 50×30 **c** 90×20 **d** 30×60
   e 60×60 **f** 80×50 **g** 20×60 **h** 70×90

2 Three answers are given for each calculation. Which is correct?

   a 40×70 280, 2800, 28 000   **b** 200×40 800, 8000, 80 000

3 Work out each of these.

    a $200 \div 50$ **b** $1000 \div 20$ **c** $600 \div 40$ **d** $2000 \div 50$

    e $1800 \div 100$ **f** $1600 \div 40$ **g** $2400 \div 80$ **h** $3500 \div 50$

4 Estimate the answer to each of these.

    a 18×28 **b** 13×42 **c** 53×48 **d** 77×33 **e** 91×58

5 Estimate the answer to each of these.

    a $901 \div 29$ **b** $487 \div 21$ **c** $1032 \div 48$ **d** $1820 \div 32$

    e $1784 \div 96$

6 **a** One box contains 32 pipe cleaners. Estimate the number of pipe cleaners contained in 17 boxes.

    b Some local football teams have 11 players. There are 286 players altogether. How many teams are there?

Practice

9F Calculating with measurements

1 Convert the following measurements.

    a 160 mm to cm   **b** 0.53 m to cm   **c** 0.035 km to m

    d 9.7 m to cm   **e** 5200 m to km   **f** 37 m to km

    g 4000 cm to km   **h** 23 cm to mm   **i** 8.25 m to mm

    j 9 km to cm   **k** 3400 g to kg   **l** 9.32 kg to g

    m 265 g to kg   **n** 0.01 kg to g   **o** 9 g to kg

    p 3200 ml to l   **q** 5.729 l to ml

    r 115 minutes to hours/minutes   **s** 924 minutes to hours/minutes

2 Add together the following measurements and give the answer in an appropriate unit.

    a 0.063 kg, 580 g, 0.4 kg   **b** 450 ml, 0.63 l, 9 cl

    c 640 mm, 94 cm, 0.003 km

3 Fill in the missing unit.

    a A car weighs 1262 ...

    b A £1 coin is about 3 ... thick.

    c A wine glass holds about 30 ... of wine.

    d Scott ran 200 ... in a time of 32 ...

Practice

10A Square numbers

1 Which of these numbers are **not** square?

77 1
27 36
9
0 64 59
2
100
80

2 a Copy and continue the pattern to make eight rows. Work out all of the answers.

$$1 = $$
$$1 + 3 = $$
$$1 + 3 + 5 = $$
$$1 + 3 + 5 + \ldots = $$

b What can you say about the answers?

3 a Copy and continue the pattern to make six rows.

$$2^2 - 1^2 = \qquad 4 - 1 = 3$$
$$3^2 - 2^2 = \qquad 9 - 4 = 5$$
$$4^2 - 3^2 = \qquad =$$
$$5^2 - 4^2 = \qquad =$$

b What can you say about the answers?
c Can you find a rule that gives the answer? Check that your rule works for $10^2 - 9^2$.

Practice

. 10B Triangle numbers

1 Which of the following numbers are **not** triangular?

5 10 36
40 3 18 2
21
45 8
6

2 Look at the numbers in the box. Write down the numbers from the box that are:

    a square numbers   **b** triangle numbers
    c odd numbers   **d** multiples of 3
    e factors of 48   **f** prime numbers

> 1, 2, 3, 4, 5, 6, 13, 16, 18, 21, 22, 36, 40, 41, 45

3 Each of the following numbers is the sum of two triangle numbers. Write them down, e.g. 16 = 1 + 15.

    a 4   **b** 18   **c** 38   **d** 42   **e** 70

Practice

10C From mappings to graphs

1 For each of the following

    i   complete the input/output diagram.
    ii complete the coordinates alongside.
    iii plot the coordinates and draw the graph.

a | × 4 | **Coordinates**

    0 → 0   (0, 0)
    1 → 4   (1, 4)
    2 →   (2,)
    3 →   (3,)
    4 →   (4,)
    5 →   (5,)

b | × 3 | → | + 4 | **Coordinates**

    0 → 4   (0, 4)
    1 → 7   (1, 7)
    2 →   (2,)
    3 →   (3,)
    4 →   (4,)
    5 →   (5,)

c | × 3 | → | − 1 | **Coordinates**

    1 → 2   (1, 2)
    2 →   (2,)
    3 →   (3,)
    4 →   (4,)
    5 →   (5,)

2 Choose some of your own starting points and create a graph from each of the following functions.

a → +5 →

b → ×5 → −3 →

Practice

10D Naming graphs

1 Write down the name of the straight line that passes through each of these pairs of points.

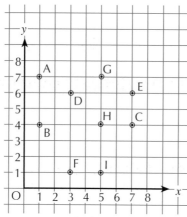

a A and G	**b** E and C	**c** B and H
d D and F	**e** C and E	**f** F and I

2 Draw the following graphs on the same grid. Label each line.

Use these axes:
x-axis from 0 to 8
y-axis from 0 to 8

a $y = 2$	**b** $x = 2$	**c** $y = 8$
d $x = 6$	**e** $y = 5$	**f** $x = 7$

3 Write down the letters which lie on the following lines.

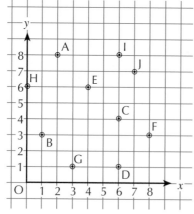

a $x = 4$	**b** $y = 3$	**c** $x = 2$
d $y = 6$	**e** $x = 8$	**f** $y = 1$

10E Naming sloping lines

1 Copy and complete the following input/output diagram for each of the stated functions.

→ function →	Coordinates
2 →	(2,)
3 →	(3,)
4 →	(4,)
5 →	(5,)
6 →	(6,)

a → + 1 → **b** → – 1 → **c** → + 2 → **d** → – 2 →

2 **a** Plot each set of coordinates from Question 1 on the same axes.

Use these axes:
x-axis from 0 to 7
y-axis from 0 to 7

b Match each line to one of the following equations.
$y = x - 1$ $y = x + 2$ $y = x - 2$ $y = x + 1$

3 Answer these questions without drawing graphs.

a Is the point (3, 6) on the graph of $y = 2x$?
b Is the point (20, 16) on the graph of $y = x - 6$?
c Is the point (5, 17) on the graph of $y = 3x + 2$?
d Is the point (9, 76) on the graph of $y = 10x - 14$?

4 Which of the following lines does the point (5, 9) lie on?

$y = 4x$ $y = x + 3$ $y = 2x - 1$ $y = 5$

1 Measure the size of each of the following angles, giving your answers to the nearest degree.

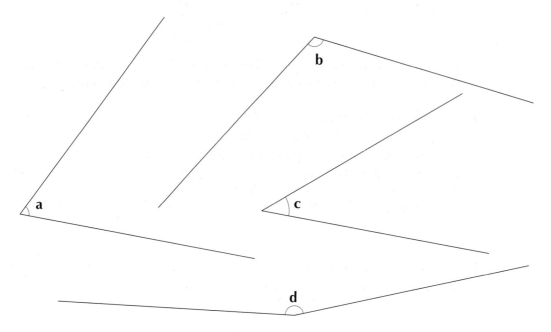

2 Draw and label the following angles.
   a 70°   **b** 45°   **c** 135°   **d** 26°   **e** 152°

3 **a** Measure all the angles in the quadrilateral ABCD.
   b Add the angles together.
   c Comment on your answer.

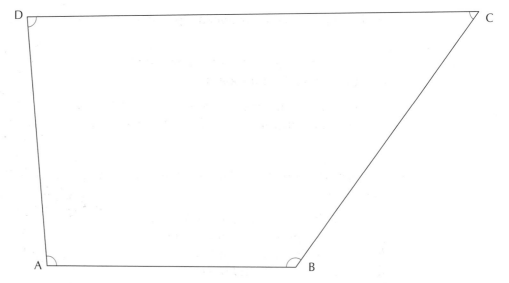

Practice

11B Constructions

1 Construct the following triangles. Remember to label the vertices and angles.

a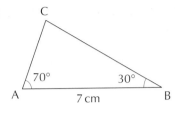

b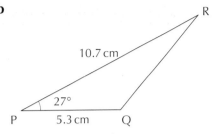

c On your drawing, measure sides BC and AC to the nearest millimetre.
d On your drawing, measure ∠Q and ∠R to the nearest degree.

2 a Construct the quadrilateral PQRS. Draw PQ first, then RQ, then SP.
b On your drawing, measure ∠R and ∠S, to the nearest degree.
c On your drawing, measure RS, to the nearest millimetre.

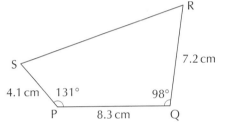

3 a Construct the triangle ABC with AB = 6.4 cm, BC = 11.3 cm, ∠B = 16°.
b Measure side AC, to the nearest millimetre.
c Measure ∠A and ∠C, to the nearest degree.

Practice

11C Solving geometrical problems

1 Draw the different types of quadrilateral, e.g. square, rectangle, etc. Draw one diagonal for each quadrilateral. Describe the triangles you have made.

2 Explain the difference between a parallelogram and a trapezium.

3 How many different kinds of quadrilateral can be constructed on this pin-board?

Use square dotted paper to record your quadrilaterals. Beneath each diagram, write the name of the quadrilateral.

4 A square is a special kind of rectangle. Fill in the blanks to make different statements.

a A parallelogram is a special kind of …
b A … is a special kind of parallelogram.
c A square is a special kind of …
d A … is a special kind of kite.

12A Percentages

1 Write down or work out the equivalent percentage and decimal to each of these fractions.

   a $\frac{1}{2}$ **b** $\frac{6}{10}$ **c** $\frac{1}{4}$ **d** $\frac{4}{5}$

2 Write down or work out the equivalent percentage and fraction to each of these decimals.

   a 0.4   **b** 0.9   **c** 0.75   **d** 0.1

3 Write down or work out the equivalent fraction and decimal to each of these percentages.

   a 25%   **b** 60%   **c** 70%   **d** 20%

4 Without using a calculator, work out each of these.

   a 10% of 400   **b** 25% of 12   **c** 20% of 70   **d** 50% of 126

5 Work out each of these.

   a 75% of 200 kg   **b** 30% of 60 m   **c** 15% of 80 years
   d 35% of 17 litres   **e** 55% of 4200 seeds **f** 95% of 634 houses

6 Which is bigger?

   a 20% of £73 or 35% of £56   **b** 10% of 523 g or 95% of 46 g

12B Ratio and proportion

1 a For each of these shapes, work out the proportion that is shaded.

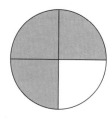 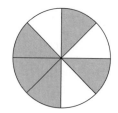 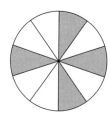

  b For each shape, complete these statements.

> There are ... parts shaded out of ... parts altogether.

> ... in every ... parts are shaded.

2 The contents of two boxes of muesli are shown below.

Luxury Muesli
Oats	150g
Wheat	60g
Nuts	270g
Fruit	120g

Natural Breakfast
Oats	280g
Wheat	240g
Nuts	200g
Fruit	80g

a What is the total weight of each box?

b Copy and complete the table below, which shows the proportion of each ingredient.

	Oats	Wheat	Nuts	Fruit
Luxury Muesli	25%			
Natural Breakfast				

3 5 reels of fishing line have a total length of 70 m. What is the total length of

a 3 reels **b** 11 reels?

4 Look at the squares below. 1 in every 6 squares is black.

Copy and complete the table.

Number of black squares	Number of white squares
1	5
2	10
3	
5	
8	
	50
	60
	100

5 On a draughts board, there are 2 black pieces for every 1 white piece. There are 18 pieces on the board.

a How many black pieces are there?

b What proportion of the pieces is white?

12C Calculating ratios and proportions

1 Reduce each of the following ratios to its simplest form.

a $9:6$ **b** $8:20$ **c** $24:30$ **d** $200:900$

e $75:45$ **f** $21:56$

2 Write down the ratio of coloured : white squares for these grids.

a 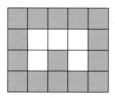   **b**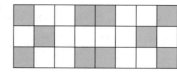

3 Four football teams scored 250 goals altogether. Beetwood Rangers scored 50 goals, Trenton FC 35, Middleton Wanderers 90 and Pinkhams scored the rest.

a Write down the percentage of the total goals that each team scored.

b Write down each of the following goal ratios in its simplest form.

   i Beetwood Rangers : Trenton FC

   ii Middleton Wanderers : Pinkhams

   iii Pinkhams : Beetwood Rangers

4 The atmosphere of Uranus is made up of Hydrogen and other gases in the ratio $6:1$. A space probe filled two flasks with samples of the atmosphere.

a One flask contained 18 litres of Hydrogen. How much other gases did it contain?

b One flask contained $\frac{1}{2}$ litre of other gases. How much Hydrogen did it contain?

12D Solving ratio and proportion problems

1 In the pattern below, 1 match in every 3 is unused. The proportion of unused matches is $\frac{1}{3}$.

a What is the proportion of used matches?

b Copy and complete the table.

Unused matches	Used matches	Total matches
1	2	3
2	4	
3		
6		
	20	

c If you know the number of unused matches, how would you work out the number of used matches?

d If you know the number of used matches, how would you work out the number of unused matches?

e If you know the total number of matches, how would you work out the number of unused matches?

f If you know the total number of matches, how would you work out the number of used matches?

2 Divide £180 in each of these ratios.

    a 4 : 5   **b** 11 : 4   **c** 5 : 7

3 Andrea divides up her free time in the ratio

> sewing : reading = 7 : 3

She has 300 minutes of free time. How much time does she spend on each activity?

4 There are 96 houses on an estate. The ratio of detached to semi-detached houses is 1 : 5. How many of each kind of house are there?

5 Dominic has 30 coloured sweets left in a packet. These are in the ratio

> red : green = 2 : 3

    a How many of each colour are there?

    b If he eats 2 red sweets and 3 green sweets, what is the new ratio red : green? Comment on your answer.

CHAPTER 13 Algebra 4

Practice   **13A Solving 'brick wall' problems**

Find the unknown number *x* in each of these 'brick wall' problems.

1

30	
x	9	5

2

21	
x	8	3

3

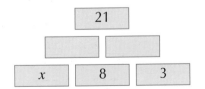

4

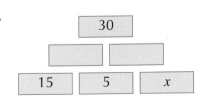

5

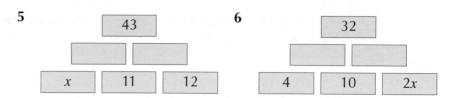

6

Practice

13B Solving square-and-circle problems

1 Find the values of A, B, C and D in each of these square-and-circle puzzles.

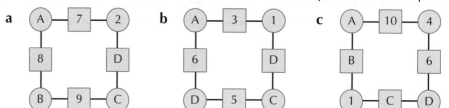

2 **a** When A = 5, write down the values of B, C, D and E.
b When A = 9, write down the values of B, C, D and E.
c When A = 3, write down the values of B, C, D and E.

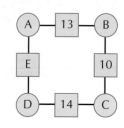

Practice

13C Using algebra to solve problems

Write an equation for each question. Then solve your equation.

Example

A mug holds 7 cl more than a cup. A mug and a cup have a total capacity of 39 cl. What is the capacity of a cup?

Working   Let x be the capacity of a cup.

The capacity of a mug is then $x + 7$.

So $x + x + 7 = 39$

$2x + 7 = 39$

$2x = 39 - 7$

$2x = 32$

$x = 16$

Answer   A cup holds 16 cl.

1 Sonja is 4 years older than Hing Wai. Their ages total 18 years. How old is Hing Wai?

2 Large eggs weigh 8 g more than medium eggs. A large egg and a medium egg have a total weight of 72 g. What is the weight of a medium egg?

3 A pack of plasticine costs 30p more than a protractor. The two items cost £1.60 altogether. How much does a protractor cost? **Hint**: Change £1.60 to pence first.

4 The sum of two consecutive numbers is 43. Find the smaller number.

5 Dana has filled 10 pages of her exercise book. She fills 4 pages each day. Her exercise book has 54 pages. How many more days will it take her to fill her exercise book?

14. Shape, Space and Measures 4

Practice   **14A Line symmetry**

1 Copy each of these shapes and draw its lines of symmetry. Write below each shape the number of lines of symmetry it has.

a **B**   b **W**   c

d   e

2 Write down the number of lines of symmetry for each of the following shapes.

a   b   c   d

3 Copy each shape onto squared paper. Draw an extra line to make the shape have one line of symmetry.

a   b   c

1 Copy each of these shapes. Write the order of rotational symmetry beneath the shape. Mark the centre of rotation.

a   b   c   d

2 Write down the order of rotational symmetry for each of the following shapes.

a   b   c   d

3 **a** Copy each shape onto squared paper. Shade an extra square to give the shape rotational symmetry, order 2. Mark the centre of rotation.

i 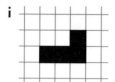 ii 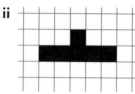 iii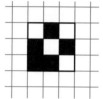

b Copy each shape onto squared paper. Shade extra squares to give the shape rotational symmetry, order 4. Mark the centre of rotation.

i 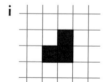 ii   iii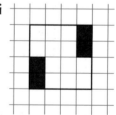

4 Draw new shapes on squared paper with the following properties.

a Rotational symmetry, order 4.
b Rotational symmetry, order 2, with no line symmetry.
c Rotational symmetry, order 2, with two lines of symmetry.
d Rotational symmetry, order 4, with four lines of symmetry.

1 Copy each of these diagrams onto squared paper and draw its reflection in the given mirror line.

a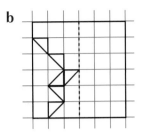

b

c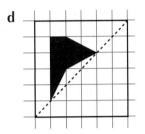

d

2 Look at the points shown on the grid below.

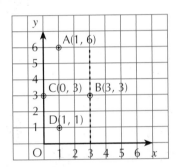

    a Copy the grid onto squared paper and plot the points A, B, C and D. Include the coordinates on your diagram. Draw the mirror line.

    b Reflect the points in the mirror line and label them A′, B′, C′ and D′.

    c Write down the coordinates of the image points.

3 The diagrams show the reflections of numbers (images). Copy each diagram. Draw the numbers (objects).

    a   b   c

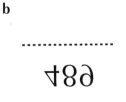

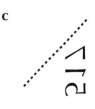

1 Copy each of the shapes below onto a square grid. Draw the image after each one has been rotated about the point marked X through the angle indicated. Use tracing paper to help.

a

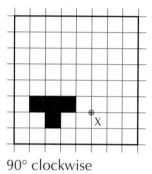

90° clockwise

b

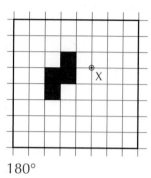

180°

c

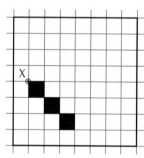

90° anti-clockwise

d

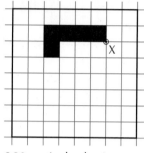

90° anti-clockwise

2 **a** Rotate the triangle ABC through 90° anti-clockwise about the point (4, 4) to give the image A'B'C'.
   b Write down the coordinates of A', B' and C'.
   c Which coordinate point remains fixed throughout the rotation?
   d Fully describe the rotation that will map the triangle A'B'C' onto the triangle ABC.

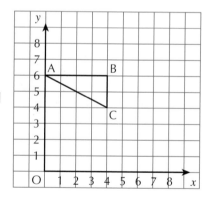

3

90° clockwise

180°

90° anti-clockwise

   a Copy each number.
   b Rotate the number through the given angle. Use the dot as the centre of rotation.

1 Describe each of the following translations.

  a A to C
  b A to D
  c C to B
  d D to E
  e B to A
  f B to D
  g D to C

2 Copy the grid and kites onto squared paper.

  a Write down the coordinates of the vertices of kite M.
  b Translate kite M 2 units left, 6 units down. Label the new kite P.
  c Write down the coordinates of the vertices of kite P.
  d Translate kite P 5 units left, 6 units up. Label the new kite Q.
  e Write down the coordinates of the vertices of kite Q.
  f Translate kite Q 1 unit right, 3 units down. Label the new kite R.
  g Write down the coordinates of the vertices of kite R.
  h Describe the translation that maps kite R onto kite S.

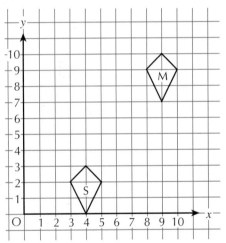

Practice

15A Pie charts

1 The table shows the favourite computer games of 40 players. Copy the circle below that is divided into ten sectors. Use this circle to draw a pie chart of the data. Remember to label your pie chart.

Computer game	No. of players
Wings	6
Venture II	12
Armageddon	8
Space Dust	4
Truckers	10

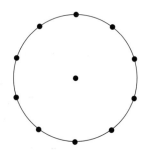

2 The tables show worldwide air pollution due to sulphur emissions for 1990 and 1999.

1990

Area of the world	Contribution to air pollution (%)
Western Europe	20
Eastern Europe	25
Asia	25
Africa	5
North America	15
Rest of the world	10

1999

Area of the world	Contribution to air pollution (%)
Western Europe	15
Eastern Europe	15
Asia	35
Africa	5
North America	15
Rest of the world	15

a Draw a pie chart for each table.
b Which areas of the world increased their proportion of world air pollution between 1990 and 1999?

c Which areas of the world decreased their proportion of world air pollution between 1990 and 1999?

d The proportion of world air pollution stayed the same for some areas of the world. Which areas?

e Do the pie charts show that there was more air pollution in 1999 compared to 1990? Explain your answer.

Practice

15B The median and the mean

1 Find the median of the following sets of data.

a 2, 7, 3, 12, 9, 15, 3
b 31, 19, 17, 28, 40, 30, 7, 12, 8

2 Find the median of the following sets of data.

a 200 mm, 150 mm, 600 mm, 300 mm, 450 mm
b £3.20, £2.90, £3.10, £3, £3.15, £2.90, £2.85
c 58 g, 48 g, 48 g, 52 g, 50 g, 51 g, 50 g, 56 g, 48 g, 58 g, 52 g, 56 g, 49 g

3 Find the mean of the following sets of data.

a 4, 7, 2, 8, 9
b 3, 15, 7, 10, 23, 4, 9, 1

4 Find the mean of the following sets of data, giving your answer to one decimal place.

a 3, 8, 4, 7, 9, 2, 4
b 53, 94, 21, 64, 10, 17, 35, 88, 42

5 The lap times (in seconds) for eight racing model cars are shown below.

17, 20, 15, 16, 20, 15, 17, 20, 67

a Find the mean lap time.
b Find the median lap time.
c Find the modal lap time.
d Which average do you think is the worst one to use? Explain your answer.
e Why are so few lap times greater than the mean?

6 Paddy's chickens laid these eggs during one week.

Monday	Tuesday	Wednesday	Thursday
7	6	8	5

a Calculate the mean eggs laid.

The chickens were moved to a different barn on Friday and laid no eggs.

b Calculate the new mean for Monday to Friday.
c Which mean describes egg-laying best? Explain your answer.

15C Statistical surveys

Write your own statistical report on one or more of the following topics.

Remember:
● Decide on your sample size.
● Decide whether you need to use a data collection sheet or a questionnaire.
● Find any relevant averages.
● Illustrate your report with suitable diagrams or graphs, and explain why you have used them.
● Write a short conclusion based on all the evidence.

The data can be collected from people in your class or year group, but it may be possible to collect the data from other sources, friends and family outside school.

1 Most people believe that eating organic vegetables will make you healthier.

Hint: Design a questionnaire.

2 On average, people can remember a number with 7 digits after seeing it once.

Hint: Design an experiment, including a data collection sheet.

3 The average number of goals scored in a football match is fewer than 2.

Hint: Use secondary data sources such as newspapers, football albums, etc.

Practice

15D More on experimental probability

1 a i Write the letters S, P, I, N, N, E, R, S on eight pieces of paper and place them in a circle. Place a bottle in the middle.

ii Copy this tally chart.

Letter	Tally	Frequency	Experimental probability	Theoretical probability
S				
P				
I				
N				
E				
R				

iii Spin the bottle 40 times and record your results in the tally chart. If the bottle stops exactly halfway between two letters, ignore the result and spin again.

iv Calculate the experimental probability for each letter. Write your answers as decimals.

v Calculate the theoretical probability for each letter. Write your answers as decimals.

b In a game, if the bottle lands on an S or N you win, otherwise you lose.

i Calculate the experimental probability of winning.

ii Calculate the theoretical probability of winning.

iii Is the game fair? Explain your answer.

CHAPTER 16 Number 5

16A Adding and subtracting decimals

1 Without using a calculator, work out each of these.

a 4.2 + 5.6 **b** 6.3 + 9.3 **c** 7.5 + 1.9
d 5.8 + 7 + 9.3 **e** 28.4 + 17 + 13.9

2 Without using a calculator, work out each of these.

a 5 − 2.7 **b** 12 − 0.4 **c** 7 − 2.6 **d** 23 − 16.1

3 a How much is left if 37 cm of wire is cut from a 3 m reel? Work in metres.

b How much is left if 180 cl of juice is poured from a jug containing 5 litres? Work in litres.

4 Lars wants to make these statues using plaster of Paris. The amount of plaster needed for each statue is shown.

Bear
2500 g

rhino
1.4 kg

pig
1800 g

dog
3.25 kg

cat
2300 g

a How much plaster of Paris does Lars need to make all the statues?

Lars has a 7 kg bag of plaster of Paris. He makes a dog and a rhino.

b How much plaster of Paris does he use?
c How much plaster does he have left over?

Practice
16B Multiplying and dividing decimals

1 Work out the following, without using a calculator.

    a 5×3.7 **b** 2.8×7 **c** 9×1.6 **d** 7.9×8

2 Work out the following, without using a calculator.

    a $8.4 \div 3$ **b** $40.6 \div 7$ **c** $49.8 \div 6$ **d** $21.6 \div 9$

3 A pack of six mini Easter eggs weighs 88.8 g. How much does one egg weigh?

4 A tank travelled 61.2 miles on 9 litres of diesel.

    a How many miles could it travel on 1 litre?
    b How many miles could it travel on 4 litres?

5 Every second, a computer downloads 3.7 kilobytes of information from the internet. How much information does it download in 8 seconds?

Practice
16C Divisibility and multiples

1 Write down all the multiples of 10 between 32 and 84.

2 Write down all the multiples of 9 between 17 and 68.

3 Circle the 3 numbers that are both multiples of 3 *and* multiples of 6.

    9   24   32   30   51   27   42

4 Copy and complete the table.

Number	Divisible by 2	Divisible by 3	Divisible by 4	Divisible by 5
26	Yes	No		
45				
84				

5 Say whether each of the following statements is true or false. If it is false, give an example to show it.

    a All multiples of 8 are also multiples of 4.
    b All multiples of 3 are odd.

Practice

16D Factors of numbers

1 Copy and complete the factor diagrams for **a** 12 **b** 16.

a 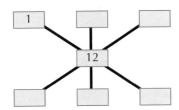 **b**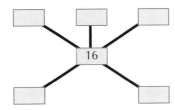

2 8 has four factors. Write them down.

3 30 has eight factors. Write them down.

4 Find all of the factors of each number.

    a 4   **b** 14   **c** 32   **d** 36   **e** 45

5 Find a prime number greater than 30.

Practice

16E Percentages of quantities

1 Match each percentage with an equivalent decimal or fraction,
e.g. 25% = 0.25.

$\frac{4}{5}$ 10% $\frac{3}{4}$ 0.3

90%

30%   50%   75%

0.1 $\frac{1}{2}$ 40% $\frac{2}{5}$ 0.9   80%

2 Calculate the following.

    a 80% of £20   **b** 25% of 80 kg   **c** 5% of £400
    d 45% of 600   **e** 15% of 120 m

3 Copy these calculations.

       ... % of 40 = 22
       ... % of 300 = 45
       ... % of 250 = 10

The missing percentages are 15%, 4% and 55%.
Complete your calculations with the correct percentages.

4 A bag contains 200 chocolate beans.

Anna eats 20% and then gives the bag to Raj.

a How many beans does Anna eat?
b How many beans does she give to Raj?

Raj eats 10% of the beans he receives.

c How many beans does Raj eat?
d How many beans does he have left?

Practice

16F Solving problems

1 a A Monford car has a fuel consumption of 68 miles per gallon. How far could it travel on 7 gallons of fuel?
b A Van Rover can travel 344 miles on 8 gallons of fuel. How far could it travel on 1 gallon?

2 Mark buys 6 cans of cola at 28p each. Lyling buys 8 cans of cola at 27p each. How much more does Lyling spend than Mark?

3 The diagram shows a length of kerb.

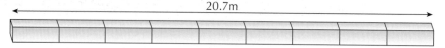

20.7m

a What is the length of one kerb stone?
b What is the total length of 6 kerb stones?

4 Anna has a £2 coin. Pens cost 23p each.

a How many pens can she buy?
b How much change would she receive?

CHAPTER

17 Algebra 5

Practice

17A Solving equations

1 Solve each of the following equations.

    a $7x = 21$ **b** $2p = 46$ **c** $9y = 36$ **d** $5T = 60$

2 Solve each of the following equations.

    a $a + 6 = 14$ **b** $d - 17 = 3$ **c** $m + 3 = 8$
    d $s - 10 = 10$ **e** $h - 10 = 3$ **f** $q + 12 = 18$

3 Solve each of the following equations.

a $2n + 7 = 25$ **b** $3k + 10 = 28$ **c** $6f + 7 = 31$

d $4g + 5 = 61$ **e** $3w + 8 = 80$ **f** $5e + 3 = 23$

g $12m + 4 = 52$ **h** $6v + 4 = 46$

4 Solve each of the following equations using number machines.

Example

$x + 3 = 51$

Working Write the equation using number machines:

$x \rightarrow \boxed{+3} \rightarrow 51$

$x \leftarrow \boxed{-3} \leftarrow 51$ (reverse the number machine: change +3 to −3)

$x = 51 - 3 = 48$ (work backwards to find the answer)

a $y + 7 = 12$ **b** $x + 5 = 34$ **c** $c - 3 = 8$

Practice

17B Formulae

1 This formula can be used to convert pounds (£) into Pesos:

$P = 6B$, where B is the number of pounds and P is the number of Pesos.

a Use the formula to convert £40 to Pesos.
b Use the formula to convert £18 to Pesos.

2 This formula is used to generate odd numbers: $m = 2n + 1$.

Find m when   **a** $n = 4$ **b** $n = 16$.

3 The time needed to roast a joint of meat is given by the formula:

$T = 30w + E$

where T is the cooking time in minutes, w is the weight of the joint in kg, and E is extra time in minutes.

a Calculate the cooking time for a joint weighing 3 kg which needs 25 minutes of extra time.
b Calculate the cooking time when $w = 2$ kg and $E = 15$.

4 *D*

This metal plate was made by cutting a square hole from a square piece of metal.

Its perimeter is given by the formula: $P = 4(D + d)$

where P is the perimeter, D is the outer side and d is the inner side.

a Calculate the perimeter when the outer side is 25 mm and the inner side is 18 mm.

b Calculate the perimeter when $D = 46$ mm and $d = 25$ mm.

Practice

17C A square investigation

Each shape is made using an inner square and an outer square. The side of the outer square is shown below each shape.

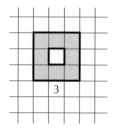
3

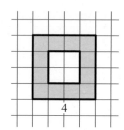
4

1 Copy this table.

Side of outer square, s			3	4	5	6	7	8
Number of shaded squares, n								

2 Count the numbers of shaded squares and write them in your table.

3 Draw more shapes to complete the table.

4 What do you notice about the numbers of shaded squares in the table?

5 Write down a rule that gives the number of shaded squares, n, if you are told the side, s. **Hint**: Start by multiplying by 4.

6 Write your rule as a formula, beginning with $n =$.

17D Graphs from the real world

1 The graph shows how long it takes for a computer printer to print a number of photos. Use the graph to answer the following questions.

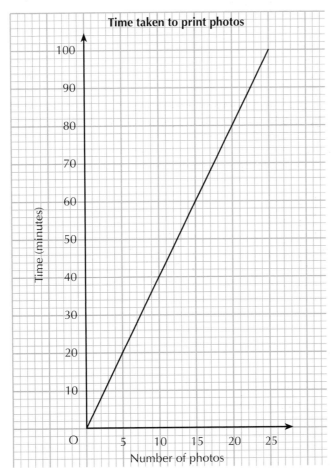

a How long does it take to print **i** 10 photos **ii** 22 photos?
b How many photos can be printed in **i** 80 minutes **ii** 48 minutes?

2 A clothing mail order company charges £2.50 per item for postage and packing.

a Copy and complete the table.

Number of items	2	4	6	8	10	12	14
Postage & packing (£)			15				

b Draw a graph of the data using these scales:
  x-axis (Number of items)   2 cm to 2 items
  y-axis (Postage & packing)   2 cm to £5
  Use your graph to answer the following questions.
c What is the postage and packing charge for **i** 6 items **ii** 13 items?
d How many items can be delivered for a postage and package charge of
  i £10 **ii** £27.50?

Practice

17E Triangle-and-circle problems

1 Using these numbers,

2 3 4 5 6 7

arrange them in a triangle that gives each of these totals.

a /15\   **b** /14\   **c** /12\

2 Using the above numbers, it is impossible to find the triangle /16\ .
Explain why.

CHAPTER

18 Shape, Space and Measures 5

Practice

18A Polygons

1 **a** 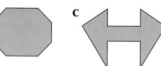 **b** **c**   **d** **e**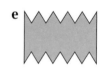

    i Name each polygon, e.g. heptagon.
    ii Which polygons are regular?
    iii Describe each polygon as concave or convex.

2 Draw these polygons.

    a A pentagon with one right-angle and one reflex angle.
    b A hexagon with rotational symmetry, order 2.
    c An octagon with exactly two lines of symmetry.
    d A hexagon with one line of symmetry and two reflex angles.

3 Use squared paper to draw 8 different kinds of polygon
inside a 3 by 3 grid. Use a different grid for each polygon.
Describe each polygon, e.g. convex quadrilateral.

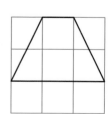

Practice

18B Tessellations

Make a tessellation from each of the following shapes, if possible. Use a square grid to help.

a   b   c   d

Practice

18C Constructing 3-D shapes

1 Which of the following are nets for the cuboid shown?

a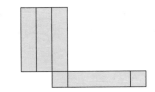

b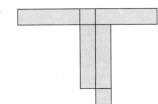

c

2 Which of the following are nets for the half cylinder shown?

a   b   c   d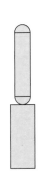

3 Stick a photocopy or a tracing of this net on to a sheet of thin card. Cut out around the net shape. Fold and glue it to make the box.

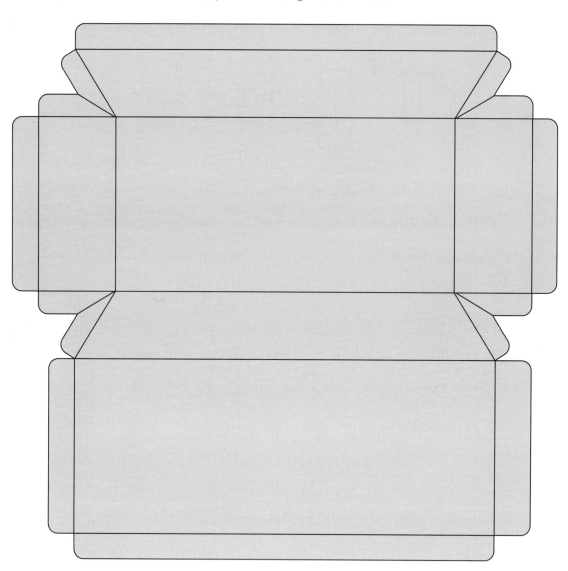

Published by HarperCollins*Publishers* Limited
77–85 Fulham Palace Road
Hammersmith
London
W6 8JB

www.**Collins**Education.com
Online support for schools and colleges

10 9 8 7 6 5 4 3 2

ISBN 0 00 713868 7

British Library Cataloguing in Publication Data
A Catalogue record for this publication is available from the British Library

Commissioned by Mark Jordan
Edited by Angus Boyd-Heron
Typesetting and design by Derek Lee
Project Management by Angus Boyd-Heron
Covers by Tim Byrne
Illustrations by Derek Lee
Additional proofreading by Sam Holmes and Helen Parr
Production by Jack Murphy
Printed and bound by Scotprint

The publishers would like to thank the many teachers and advisers whose feedback helped to shape *Maths Frameworking*.

You might also like to visit:
www.**fire**and**water**.com
The book lover's website